Y0-AGL-516

# Snoopy and
# The Great Pumpkin

Will Linus Finally See The Great Pumpkin?

Based on the comic strip "Peanuts"
Created and Written by:
Charles M. Schulz

Produced and Directed by:
Lee Mendelson
Desirée Goyette

Original Music and Lyrics by:
Desirée Goyette

Music Arranged and Conducted by:
Ed Bogas

Art Director:
Frank Hill

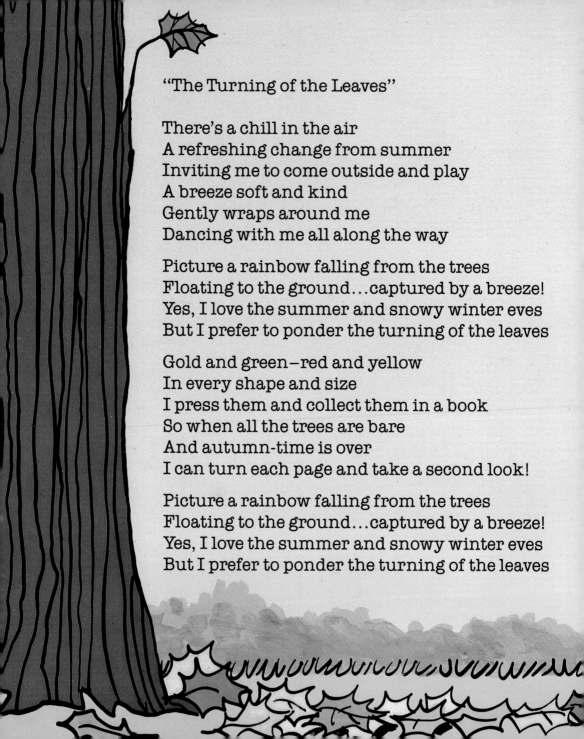

"The Turning of the Leaves"

There's a chill in the air
A refreshing change from summer
Inviting me to come outside and play
A breeze soft and kind
Gently wraps around me
Dancing with me all along the way

Picture a rainbow falling from the trees
Floating to the ground…captured by a breeze!
Yes, I love the summer and snowy winter eves
But I prefer to ponder the turning of the leaves

Gold and green—red and yellow
In every shape and size
I press them and collect them in a book
So when all the trees are bare
And autumn-time is over
I can turn each page and take a second look!

Picture a rainbow falling from the trees
Floating to the ground…captured by a breeze!
Yes, I love the summer and snowy winter eves
But I prefer to ponder the turning of the leaves

"The Great Pumpkin"

Every year in October on Halloween night
There appears an incredible sight
I sit and wait in the pumpkin patch
Under the pale moonlight

And just when he thinks I'm not looking
Or when I am blinking my eyes
As fast as a flash and as quiet as night
From this pumpkin patch he will rise!

I sit every year in the pumpkin patch
Beside my sweet babboo
We wait and wait in the chilly air
Until I'm so cold I turn blue!

She pretends to believe him
So she can sit with him all alone
But I get so tired and cold and bored
That I wish he'd give up and go home!

He will appear only if you are sincere
And if you believe in the wonderful things he can do!
Well, if he's such a wonderful guy, please tell us why
The only one who believes in him is you!

Someday he'll show up
And then you will know I am right!
Yes, perhaps he'll show up!
Maybe tonight is the night!

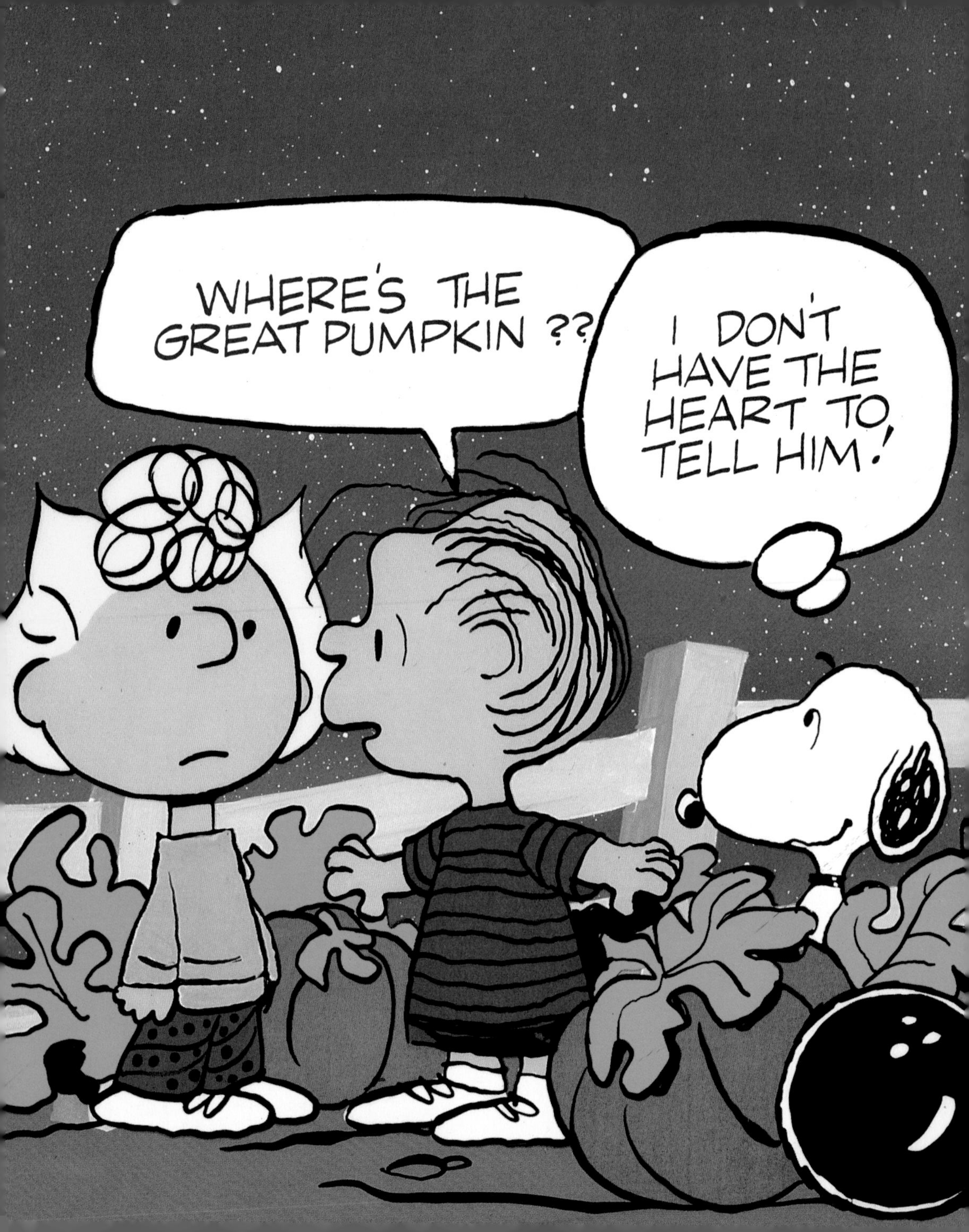
WHERE'S THE GREAT PUMPKIN ??
I DON'T HAVE THE HEART TO TELL HIM!

"Lighten Up"

Ya gotta lighten up–lighten up
Things'll be much better if you lighten up!
Don't waste your time
Wonderin' what went wrong
Lighten up–lighten up
Just lighten up!

Ya gotta lighten up–lighten up
Forget about what happened
And just brighten up
It does no good to frown
About what's going down
So just lighten up–lighten up!

We all make mistakes, you know
If we didn't, none of us would grow
So look to the days ahead
Get rid of the doubt and dread
And just try to do better instead

Ya gotta lighten up–lighten up!
You'll only make it worse
If you tighten up
One day we'll think about it
And we'll all laugh
So lighten up–lighten up!